The

"A cabbage hat,
a cabbage hat!
Will you buy
a cabbage hat?"

"It's got caterpillars.
I can't wear that.
I will not buy
a cabbage hat."

3

"A cactus hat,
a cactus hat!
Will you buy
a cactus hat?"

"It prickles and tickles.
I can't wear that.
I will not buy
a cactus hat."

5

"A goldfish hat,
a goldfish hat!
Will you buy
a goldfish hat?"

"It drips down my neck.
I can't wear that.
I will not buy
a goldfish hat."

"A fat-cat hat,
a fat-cat hat!
Will you buy
a fat-cat hat?"

"There's a purr in its fur.
I can't wear that.
I will not buy
a fat-cat hat."

"Here's a hat
that you should try.
Here's a hat
I'm sure you'll buy.

HAT SALE

11

"A jellybean hat,
a jellybean hat!
Will you buy
a jellybean hat?"

MR. GUMBY

"Jellybeans are sweet.
Jellybeans are neat.
Yes, I'll try it!
Yes, I'll buy it!

"Yes, I'll wear a jellybean hat!"